Blairsville Junior High School
Blairsville, Pennsylvania

5367

616.86   Houser, Norman
H   W.

Drugs; facts on
their use and
abuse

DATE			
APR 6	MAY 15	OCT	SEP 16 '83
APR 21	MAY 9	NOV 5	OCT 18 83
MAY 2		FEB 13 '81	DEC 8 '83
NOV 29	JAN 29	MAR 30 '81	FEB 12
DEC 18	OCT 22	FEB 23 '82	MAR 1
APR 10	APR 7	MAR 23 '82	
MAY 14	MAY 12	NOV 1	
MAY 2	MAY 12	JAN 19 '83	MAR 1
SEP 12	MAR 12	FEB 11	MAY 14
MAR 10	APR 23	FEB 24	MAY 28
	MAY 8	MAR 23 '83	FEB 27
			MR 06 01

FEB 27   5367

Blairsville Junior High School
Blairsville, Pennsylvania

© THE BAKER & TAYLOR CO.

Drugs

Facts on Their Use and Abuse

Norman W. Houser
In consultation with
Julius B. Richmond, M.D.

Hal Kearney, Art Director

Ed Bedno, Designer

Jane Bedno, Illustrator

Lothrop, Lee & Shepard Co.

New York

Norman W. Houser
Director, Inner City Project, San Diego, California.
Formerly Curriculum Specialist of Secondary
Education, San Diego Public Schools; high-school
principal and vice-principal; teacher, counselor, and
guidance-department worker at junior and senior
high school levels.

Julius B. Richmond, M.D.
Dean, The College of Medicine, State University of
New York; Professor and Chairman, Department of
Pediatrics, Upstate Medical Center, Syracuse, New
York. First Director of Project Head Start, Office of
Economic Opportunity, Washington, D.C.
Formerly Director, Institute for Juvenile Research,
Chicago, Illinois.

Special acknowledgment is made to
Orvis A. Harrelson, M.D.
Director of Health Services, Tacoma Public Schools,
Tacoma, Washington, for critical evaluation.

Mrs. Thelma Dimmitt
for editorial research and assistance.

Trade Edition First Published 1969.
Copyright © 1969 by Scott, Foresman and Company,
Glenview, Illinois 60025.
Philippines Copyright 1969 by
Scott, Foresman and Company.
Library of Congress Catalog Card Number: 74-82103
All Rights Reserved.
Printed in the United States of America.
Third printing, July 1970

Contents

A Look at the Problem

Many young people are experimenting with and using drugs and chemicals today. The problem of drug abuse exists in one form or another at all income levels and in cities, suburbs, and to a lesser degree in rural areas. Misuse of drugs is found among the uneducated and the well-educated and can cause serious harm to the individual and to society.

The misuse of drugs is often illegal and the penalties are generally severe. Nevertheless, there is increasing abuse of substances that

    intoxicate

    stimulate

    depress

    confuse

    cause hallucinations

    and, in general, disorganize the personality,

so that actions and reactions are

    foggy

    sluggish

    erratic

    violent

    irresponsible

    bizarre

    uninhibited or otherwise abnormal.

The results can be dangerous to everybody.

Chemicals and the Body

The human body reacts in a great number of ways to chemicals with which it comes in contact. In varying degrees this happens whether the chemical is applied to the skin, or is swallowed, inhaled, or injected. Chemicals may be used to stimulate or depress, to soothe or irritate, to promote growth or retard it, to stimulate or befuddle the mind, to heal or to kill. In fact, chemicals may be used to change or modify the function of almost every bodily system.

Reactions to the same chemical may vary greatly from one individual to another, or for that matter, in the same individual at different times. A life-saving antibiotic or sulfa drug must not be used with certain persons who are allergic to it; some other individuals may not experience the maximum benefits expected from a drug, because after repeated doses the body builds up a tolerance to it, and the original effectiveness of the drug is reduced.

It is important to remember that the chemistry of each person's body is different and infinitely complicated. While research has uncovered a great deal about the effects on the body of many of the chemicals found in modern drugs, there is still much to be learned in this area.

Many new chemical mixtures and compounds, some derived from a natural source and others made in laboratories, will be developed in the future. Some of these discoveries will contribute to our well-being while others will not. The task of developing and testing the effectiveness and safety of these discoveries is the vital work of research laboratories, pharmaceutical houses, and other qualified organizations.

Most of Us Are Drug Users

There are thousands of chemical substances in approved use today, by medical prescription and over-the-counter sale. These substances are intended to prevent, improve, or cure some undesirable physical or mental condition. Most, if not all, of us consume some of these drugs.

Sales are huge of such *over-the-counter* products as aspirin, mouthwashes, cough drops and syrups, eye and nose drops, athlete's foot remedies, acne controls, laxatives, vitamins and tonics, and reducing pills.

In addition to these common items, which contain various and assorted chemical substances, there are the *prescription drugs*. These drugs can be purchased legally only with a physician's prescription. They include antibiotics, antihistamines, hormones, and an almost limitless number of compounds and mixtures.

Precautions and Safety

The United States Food and Drug Administration (FDA) establishes standards not only for the manufacture of over-the-counter and prescription drugs but also for their packaging and labeling. A surprising amount of information about the product can be found on the label of the package and on the printed matter inserted in the package. It is there because the FDA requires it to be. Doctors and drug-administration officials know that drugs must be taken with caution if undesirable results are to be avoided. Information about the drug is essential if it is to be used with safety. Package labels or accompanying printed matter contain such information as this:

NAME AND DESCRIPTION:
The established chemical name of the *active* ingredients (and in some cases the *inactive* components), as well as a physical-chemical description of the product if it has some connection with the product's effectiveness.

ACTIONS:
A statement of possible effects or side effects on the user, such as increase in heartbeat, dizziness, drowsiness.

INDICATIONS:
The uses for which the drug is intended.

CONTRAINDICATIONS:
Absolute and specific situations or conditions under which the drug must not be taken, as in the case of a laxative if there are abdominal pains.

WARNINGS:
Statements about possible dangers or hazards that might develop, such as a decrease in mental alertness that would affect the user's ability to operate machinery or his ability to drive competently.

PRECAUTIONS:
Special care that should be observed under normal or unusual conditions.

ADVERSE REACTIONS:
Side effects or undesirable results that are possible or probable, such as nausea.

DOSAGE AND ADMINISTRATION:
Recommended amounts and methods for taking the drug, the frequency of use, and different dosages for adults and children.

All the above information is to ensure that the drug will be used safely. To some degree, however, the use of any drug is unpredictable because of the differences in the body chemistry of those who use it.

Drug Users and Drug Abusers— How They Differ

When a drug *user* employs the drug properly, he is doing so to prevent, improve, or cure some undesirable physical or mental condition.
He takes the drug
>   with attention to proper strength, quantity, and frequency as indicated on the prescription or label
>   for the purpose and in the manner for which the drug is intended
>   with due attention to any warnings or precautionary statements from the physician or drug manufacturer
>   after obtaining it in a legal manner.

When a drug *abuser* takes a drug, however, he disregards the items mentioned above and takes the drug for some purpose besides a particular medical condition.
He takes the drug
>   for "kicks," as a dare, to escape, to belong
>   without regard for medically prescribed dosages

often with no knowledge of the purity or strength of the drug—nor might the person from whom he obtained it have this knowledge
in violation of state and Federal laws
often after getting the drug illegally.

Dangerous Drugs and Other Chemical Substances

There are five principal categories of drugs and other chemical substances that are most often abused. They are classed rather loosely under the broad headings of *stimulants, depressants, hallucinogens, narcotics,* and *volatile chemicals.* Many of these have familiar names, but it would be difficult to list all the pills, powders, plants, fumes, and liquids now being experimented with in an effort to produce some abnormal physical or psychological sensation.

Abuse of certain of these substances can cause injury to vital organs of the body, including the liver, heart, kidneys, and brain.

Abuse can also lead to drug dependence.
DRUG DEPENDENCE
Formerly, the words *addiction* and *habituation* were used to describe an abuser's need for *repeated use* of some substance. But these terms caused confusion and they did not describe the medical aspects of the problem. Now, the World Health Organization's Expert Committee on Addiction-Producing Drugs recommends the use of the term *drug dependence* instead of "drug addiction" or

"drug habituation." This committee describes *drug dependence* as a "state of psychic [psychological] or physical dependence, or both, on a drug, arising in a person following administration of that drug on a periodic or continuous basis." Different types and degrees of dependence result from the use of different substances.

PHYSICAL DEPENDENCE

Physical dependence was known in the past as "addiction." Two conditions characterize physical dependence. They are *tolerance* and *withdrawal illness.*

Tolerance is a condition in which the body adapts itself to a drug and thus becomes able to withstand original-sized doses with diminishing effect. To maintain the same degree of reaction, the doses must therefore be continuously increased.

Withdrawal illness results when the body is forced to function without a drug it has become accustomed to and dependent upon. After the body cells have adjusted to the continued presence of a toxic substance like a drug, they react in a characteristic and extremely painful manner when the drug is withheld.

Both tolerance and withdrawal illness are *physical* in nature and do respond to medical treatment. Physical dependence is, nonetheless, a serious problem. When physical dependence is present, the motive for using the drug is not only pleasure from its use but also the avoidance of pain resulting from withdrawal. Even under medical supervision, where the amount of drugs given is gradually reduced, withdrawal is a harrowing experience.

The situation is further complicated because the abuser also usually develops an emotional need to return to the drug, even after a period of disuse and physical recovery. This need results in a situation in which there are few *permanent* cures.

PSYCHOLOGICAL DEPENDENCE

The term *psychological dependence* has a meaning similar to the term *habituation.* Very simply, it means that the use of the substance has become a habit. It may range all the way from a fairly mild, though persistent, desire for the drug to an uncontrollable craving for it. The seriousness of psychological dependence is too frequently underestimated, probably because the agonizing physical effects of withdrawal illness do not occur when the drug is withheld from the user. By any standards, however, psychological dependence must be considered as a very difficult problem to overcome.

The degree of psychological dependence varies with the drug and with the body chemistry and personality of the user. When an abuser finds that the use of a drug satisfies a craving or produces a sensation he enjoys, he may find that he develops an uncontrollable need to get the drug regardless of cost, legal penalty, or the resulting damage to mind and body. The use of the drug may so change an individual's interests, pride, motivation, and other drives and values that little or nothing is left in his psychological make-up to help him fight for a return to a normal, healthy, useful existence. Psychological dependence is very serious, very difficult to treat, and possibly incurable in many instances.

INTERRELATIONSHIP OF DRUG DEPENDENCE

While there are some differences between physical and psychological dependence on drugs, remember this:

Both types of dependence are often inter-related.

We are lacking in much of the medical and psychiatric "know-how" needed to deal with drug dependence.

Except in rare instances, such as a person's becoming accidentally dependent upon a pain-killing drug when seriously ill or injured, none of us need ever have to cope with a problem of psychological or physical drug dependence in our own lives

unless

we intentionally choose to risk the possibility by experimenting with those substances that we know have led many to such dependence.

9

The *stimulants*, such as amphetamines, and the *depressants*, such as barbiturates, are sometimes called the up-and-down drugs. This is because the stimulants *speed up* and the depressants *slow down* the action of the central nervous system. As prescribed medically, both can be useful. But both have a potential for dependence.

Statistics involving the use and abuse of stimulants and depressants are staggering. Only estimates are available, but the U.S. Bureau of Narcotics and Dangerous Drugs whose business it is to evaluate the situation indicate that over 10 million people in this country use amphetamines and barbiturates which they obtain *legally* by prescription. Abusers of these drugs may number up to another half million persons, who spend 25 million dollars yearly on amphetamines and barbiturates that they obtain *illegally*.

It is estimated that about 20 per cent of the barbiturates and over 40 per cent of the amphetamines manufactured yearly in the United States find their way into illegal outlets.

Stimulants: Amphetamines

Most of the stimulant drugs available to abusers are in the *amphetamine* group and have the characteristic of being able to stimulate directly the central nervous system. By stimulating the nervous system, this kind of drug produces a feeling of general well-being, energy, alertness, and endurance.

DESCRIPTION AND IDENTIFICATION

Because they keep the user unusually alert, awake, and active, amphetamines are often called "pep pills." The amphetamines have been misused by students cramming for exams and by truck drivers trying to stay awake on long night hauls. Both of these uses can have dangerous consequences and can lead to the dependence to which abusers are susceptible.

Nicknames for the amphetamines include such terms as "wake-ups," "eye openers," "copilots," and "A's." These drugs are commonly found in the form of a capsule, a powder, or a tablet.

DEPENDENCE AND OTHER
EFFECTS OF ABUSE

The use of amphetamines may result in psychological dependence. The abuser feels a strong need or desire to take the drug more and more frequently and in ever increasing amounts.

As abusers increase their dosage, the original effects of the drug are exaggerated. The abuser may eventually have to take up to 50 pep pills daily trying to attain the sensations he first had from just one or two tablets.

The dangers from amphetamine abuse are considerable. The abuser may exhibit

dryness of mouth	involuntary trembling
loss of appetite	restlessness
heavy perspiration	excitability
enlarged pupils	aggressive behavior
talkativeness	tension and anxiety
nervousness	inability to sleep.

Continued abuse or heavy doses of amphetamines can cause

    high blood pressure
    irregular heart rhythms or heart attacks
    paranoid delusions
    suicidal attempts.

In some very serious cases, there is a drug-
induced mental illness resembling *schizophrenia*, which is characterized by unpredictable behavior and a tendency to withdraw
from reality.

Occasionally, an overweight person whose
doctor may have prescribed an amphetamine
to help in a weight-reduction program hoards
a supply of the drug. Then, by using the drug
in a manner contrary to the physician's direc-
tions, the person may become a drug abuser
and develop psychological dependence.

A very dangerous abuse of amphetamines
occurs when truck drivers take them so they
can drive without sleep for long periods.
The use of pep pills does not magically eliminate fatigue, but simply permits the body to
use energy reserves which may suddenly and
without warning be exhausted. When the
effects of the drug wear off, the body is
brought to a state of near collapse and the
mind to a "blackout" condition. On the highway this can mean death.

There is also the danger that the ampheta-
mine-using driver may suffer from hallucinations which distort what he sees and result
in erratic and hazardous driving behavior.
Most states have laws prohibiting people
from driving while under the influence of
narcotics and dangerous drugs. Still there are
many accidents caused by such drivers.

*METHAMPHETAMINE HYDROCHLORIDE
("SPEED")*

As you can tell by looking at its chemical
name, *methamphetamine hydrochloride* is one
of the amphetamines. Its most common trade
name is Methedrine, and it has recently been
tagged by abusers with the name "Speed."

Reports are appearing in magazines and
newspapers indicating that even some drug-
sophisticated abusers are being scared away
from this drug and are wearing buttons that
read "Speed Kills." Apparently there is good
cause for such a warning. "Speed freaks" or
"meth heads" may take massive doses for
several days. During this time their behavior
may become violent, unpredictable, and dangerous to others. The abuser may have paranoid delusions and attack friends whom he
suddenly distrusts. When the abuser becomes
completely exhausted, he falls into a semi-
coma lasting a day or more and wakes in a
sluggish condition that makes him want to
start immediately on another "speed run."
Methedrine is suspected of damaging the
brain permanently, though this has not yet
been proved.

Depressants: Barbiturates

In 1903 a synthetic drug was developed
and placed on the market under the trade
name of Veronal. Its purpose was to induce
sleep. Since then nearly 2000 different *barbiturates*, commonly called sleeping pills, have
been produced. Most of these barbiturates

have names ending in the letters *al*: secobarbital, pentobarbital, amobarbital, and phenobarbital. The barbiturates are often referred to as sedatives or hypnotics. They depress the central nervous system, and they may be prescribed by a doctor to cause a patient to relax, to reduce nervousness and anxiety, or to produce sleep.

DESCRIPTION AND IDENTIFICATION

The abuser usually describes barbiturates in such general terms as "sleeping pills," "barbs," or "goofballs." Barbiturates are frequently marketed as colored pills or capsules, and specific slang terms refer to their color or are derived from their trade name. For example, yellow capsules may be known to abusers as "yellows" or "nimbies" (Nembutal). Red pills or capsules may be called "reds," "red birds," "pink ladies," or "seccys" (Seconal). The solid blue "barbs" may be described as "bluebirds," "blue angels," or just "blues." Capsules that are half red and half blue may be known as "reds and blues," "double trouble," or "rainbows."

DEPENDENCE AND OTHER EFFECTS OF ABUSE

Depressants may produce both physical and psychological dependence. Withdrawal illness from dependence on barbiturates can be more dangerous than withdrawal from narcotics. Sudden withdrawal after an extended period of abuse results in restlessness, anxiety, fear, and tremors. This is followed in a few hours by nausea, vomiting, and increasing discomfort. On the second and third day,

severe convulsions may occur. Most abusers recover from these, but some suffer an aftermath of delirium, hallucinations, and exhaustion. Continued use of the drugs may result in the following physical and mental symptoms:

slurred speech	emotional instability
loss of coördination	quarrelsomeness
staggering walk	depression
sluggishness	coma.

DEADLINESS OF DEPRESSANTS

Used properly, under medical supervision, depressants help relieve tension, nervousness, and anxiety. Used improperly, however, the barbiturates are the most *deadly* of the dangerous drugs. Statistics show that more people die as a result of acute intoxication from sleeping pills than from any other kind of drug poisoning.

Overdosage is common, because in the mental confusion that results from taking the drug, the abuser is likely to forget exactly how much he has already consumed and then proceed to take an additional amount. This may lower the activity of the breathing center to an extent that proves fatal.

Accidental overdosage through confusion is only a part of the problem, however. In addition, many deaths result from accidental swallowing as in the case of small children or deliberate overdosage as in suicide attempts.

A special hazard is involved when the abuser introduces both alcohol and barbiturates into his system. This combination, which dangerously depresses respiration, can be fatal.

In the last few years most of us have added two new words to our vocabulary, *hallucinogens* and *psychedelic*. These terms have been brought to our attention because they describe the effects on the mind of various substances popularized by drug abusers. *Hallucinogens* are substances that produce hallucinations. This simply means that a person's brain reports to him sights, sounds, and other sensory images that actually do not exist. The term *psychedelic* means mind-altering, and it refers to a mental state in which there are distorted sensations and intensified perceptions.

Various individuals or groups who wanted to experience these unreal sensations have experimented with a number of substances for their alleged mind-expanding effects. Experience has shown, however, that users of these drugs may actually lose their capability to think clearly, to reason, to create, or otherwise use their minds productively. In addition, the users of these psychedelic substances who have sought psychiatric help or have been admitted to psychiatric clinics provide proof in themselves that these substances can cause serious mental changes, violence to others, and self-destruction.

LSD (Lysergic Acid Diethylamide)

Albert Hofmann discovered the effects of LSD in 1943 after accidentally swallowing some. As a trained scientist, he carefully recorded the results of his experience.

"I noted with dismay that my environment was undergoing progressive change. Everything seemed strange and I had the greatest difficulty in expressing myself. My visual fields wavered and everything appeared deformed as in a faulty mirror. I was overcome by a feeling that I was going crazy, the worst part of it being that I was clearly aware of my condition."

Hofmann had first developed the substance in the Sandoz Pharmaceutical Laboratory in Basle, Switzerland, in 1938. He was doing research on compounds derived from the fungus *ergot*, which forms as a rust on rye, a common grain plant. Certainly he had no idea in the beginning that he had prepared one of the most powerful hallucinogenic drugs known to man. Nor could he have guessed that many young people, later to be known as "acid heads," would misuse this drug.

A LITTLE IS A LOT

From your study of science, some of you are familiar with the metric measure of weight known as a *gram*, and you may remember that it requires 28.35 grams to equal one ounce. A gram is a gigantic measurement, however, when we think of an effective dose of LSD. The average dose of LSD is from one to 250 micrograms. And a microgram is one millionth of a gram! To help in comprehending this infinitesimal weight, one imaginative person calculated that if a postage stamp were cut into 100 equal parts, each part would provide a dose of 100 micrograms for 300,000 people.

DESCRIPTION AND IDENTIFICATION

A solution of LSD is colorless, odorless, and tasteless. These qualities permit the drug to go unnoticed in or on such common objects as sugar cubes, chewing gum, blotting paper, stamps, beads, and aspirin.

DEPENDENCE AND OTHER EFFECTS OF ABUSE

There is little or no evidence that the use of LSD leads to physical dependence, but it can cause an emotional reliance that may reach a state of true psychological dependence.

The result of swallowing, inhaling, or injecting a minute quantity of LSD is known as "taking a trip." Effects of the drug begin within thirty minutes, and "trips" generally last from eight to ten hours.

LSD acts primarily on the central nervous system and may result in such physical symptoms as these:

dilated pupils
lowered temperature
chills with "goose bumps"
increased blood sugar
rapid heartbeat
increased pulse rate
nausea
loss of appetite.

Although the physical effects of LSD are slight, the effects on the mind are varied and complex. A user of LSD may experience the following:

hallucinations, such as "seeing" sounds and "tasting" colors
distorted and intensified sensory perception
reduced ability to discriminate between fact and fantasy

illusions such as objects that appear to move or melt
fear and overwhelming panic
restlessness and inability to sleep
impulses toward, and acts of, uncontrolled violence
impulses toward suicide and suicidal acts
serious mental disorders, including depression and feelings of persecution.

The above effects may vary in combination and degree from person to person and from "trip" to "trip" and may lead the user to long-term hospitalization, or in some cases death.

When death results from LSD, an indirect cause may be one of the following. With use of LSD:

Natural protective attitudes disappear.
Common sense and normal judgment are no longer present.
Ability to perceive and evaluate ordinary dangers no longer exists.

Users of LSD have been killed because they believed they could fly, and tried to, from some high elevation; or they believed they were invisible and safe from oncoming automobiles; or they performed some other strange act completely contrary to natural law and good judgment.

WHO ARE THE LSD USERS?

The LSD users can only be identified in general terms, but many of them seem to fall in the following classifications:

17-30 years old
a student or recent school dropout
from a middle- or upper-class home
having the ability and opportunity for higher education

The U.S. Food and Drug Administration indicates: "Perhaps the only common characteristic of LSD users is that they tend to make the drug the center of their universe. They talk about the drug and its effect incessantly and seek out other users as their companions."

LSD AND THE UNBORN

There is a great deal of research being done to determine the effects of LSD upon children born to mothers who have used this hallucinogen. There is evidence that LSD breaks down the chromosomes in some blood cells, causing changes much like those found in one form of leukemia. Thus mothers who have taken LSD may give birth to children with abnormal chromosomal structure. *Time Magazine* of April 19, 1968, states that "Dr. Maimon Cohen, geneticist at the State University of New York at Buffalo, reported that in a study of 220 LSD users, between 70 and 80 per cent showed chromosomal damage in their blood cells—four times the normal rate." Doctors from different parts of the country are finding similar changes, although much is still to be learned.

The warning of scientists about potential chromosome damage has kept many from experimenting with LSD. Research is also being carried on to determine whether other birth defects are caused by exposure to LSD.

Laboratory research, conducted under the controlled conditions necessary to prove cause and effect, has had to be with animals. The extent of LSD damage to litters of rats seems clearly established. But those who feel the need to be certain about humans must wait for the slow accumulation of information on babies whose mothers are identified as LSD users.

There is some evidence that repeated use of LSD may affect intelligence in certain areas. Many medical authorities feel, for example, that continued use of LSD reduces the user's ability to concentrate and think. Research on the effect of LSD is, of course, a pioneer field and much remains to be proven and discovered. What is already known, however, about the complexity and delicate functioning of the nervous system suggests caution in the use of any drugs that affect this functioning.

RECURRENCE AND LONG-RANGE EFFECTS

Long after the LSD has been taken, the user may have a totally unexpected recurrence of hallucinations. How or why this occurs is not completely understood, but the abuser who suffers this uncontrolled "flashback" may fear that he is losing his mind—which is a real possibility.

LSD users seem to exhibit an unusual characteristic which has been descriptively called a "missionary complex." They become highly persuasive and persistent in their efforts to get their loved ones (even their own very young children) and their friends to use LSD. The urging of these "missionaries" seems more effective than even the efforts of drug peddlers to get new users.

A psychological effect noticed frequently among LSD users is a change in their value systems. Those things that were formerly important to them no longer are held in esteem. Ambition dwindles, purpose is gone, and plans for careers are dropped. Included among these young people are many who at one time had exciting and promising futures but who have become members of a subculture of drug abusers whose future is indeed questionable.

THE FUTURE OF LSD

At the present time there is no legitimate manufacturer of LSD in the United States. The LSD now available has come either from secret laboratories in this country or has been smuggled in from foreign sources. Quality controls are nonexistent, and the purity and safety of the product are of no interest or concern to the manufacturer operating illegally.

When reports from psychiatric clinics began to call attention to possible irreversible organic brain damage resulting from the use of LSD, some users were undoubtedly frightened off. LSD users seemed to be more concerned about their future children than their own brain, however, and when recent studies showed that LSD can result in chromosomal breaks and potentially mentally or physically deformed children, its use in many areas of the United States was observed to drop off sharply.

When LSD was first gaining popularity, the question seemed to be whether its use would result in a "bad trip," which was a horrible, frightening, highly disturbing experience. Now that the true dangers are becoming known about the use of the hallucinogen, the question is more likely to be "Is this trip necessary?" or "Isn't any LSD trip a trap?"

Other Hallucinogens

Although LSD has received most of the publicity, there are a number of other "mind-bending" substances. Some of these are peyote, mescaline, psilocybin, psilocin, DMT, and STP.

PEYOTE AND MESCALINE

Peyote is a small cactus that grows in northern Mexico and the southwestern part of the United States. The small dome of the cactus that extends above the ground, as well as dried slices of the cactus, are called "peyote buttons" or "mescal buttons." When the "buttons" are consumed, a feeling of well-being, accompanied by vivid hallucinations, results.

The active substance of the peyote cactus is *mescaline*. Peyote has been used by Indians in North and Central America for hundreds of years for ceremonial purposes. It was not until 1896, however, that the substance mescaline was isolated from the cactus. Since then, pure mescaline has been produced in the laboratory, but much of what is used by drug abusers is in the form of ground or whole peyote buttons.

Little research has yet been done on mescaline, but it is reported by users to produce hallucinations characterized by the presence of brilliant colors.

Experiments using mescaline with pregnant hamsters resulted in an unusually large percentage of fetuses with malformations of the brain, spinal cord, liver, and other organs of the body.

PSILOCYBIN AND PSILOCIN

The psilocybe mushroom is a ritual mushroom of southern Mexico. Dr. Albert Hofmann, the discoverer of LSD, was the first to isolate two active hallucinogens in the plant. These two hallucinogens, called *psilocybin* and *psilocin*, are very similar in structure; in fact, psilocybin is converted to psilocin in the body.

Both drugs have been made in the laboratory and are said to produce brilliant visual hallucinations generally followed by a period of emotional disturbance.

DMT (DIMETHYLTRYPTAMINE)

DMT is an active hallucinogen found in a Mexican mushroom considered sacred by the Aztecs. Long before the arrival of Columbus in the Americas, certain native tribes of Mexico prepared snuff from this plant. The snuff was reported to produce convulsive movements, distortions of the body muscles, and violent behavior. Among some drug users, DMT has become a substitute for LSD, but the substance usually employed is one manufactured in a laboratory. The effects of DMT are said to be of shorter duration than those of LSD.

STP

The FDA has come up with the technical, jawbreaking name of the STP hallucinogen as 4-methyl-2, 5 dimethoxy alpha methyl phenethylamine.

The Dow Chemical Company, where the drug was first discovered, calls it DOM. DOM was developed by the Dow Chemical Company in connection with their research in the area of drugs to treat mental illness.

Users of the substance have called it *STP*, explaining that the letters stand for *S*erenity, *T*ranquillity, and *P*eace. Actually little is yet known of its specific qualities, except that it is a powerful psychedelic substance never marketed by the Dow Chemical Company, but the formula for which was probably stolen. Any prudent person would certainly avoid the use of such a powerful substance, the full effects of which have never been determined.

Other Dangerous Drugs

The thrill-seeker may have heard of Datura stramonium, MMDA, bufotenine, ZNA, as well as some common substances such as nutmeg, morning-glory seeds, toasted banana peel, and a compound known as "68." In all cases where he uses such a product, he does so blindly without any real knowledge of what the results will be. He may be taking an extremely powerful and dangerous substance on the one hand or a fraudulent one on the other. You may recall that after a lot of publicity, the claim that toasted banana peel produced hallucinogenic effects proved to be false. Likewise, the Food and Drug Administration now reports that the compound called "68" is nothing more than oil of peppermint.

As someone has very aptly suggested, the buyer/user of any unknown substance, whether it be a truly powerful one or a total fake, is being made a fool of in either case.

Is marijuana a destructive "killer weed" or a harmless "magic grass"? Without question, marijuana is the most controversial substance in drug abuse. Some facts and much fancy have been included in writings about marijuana, and it is difficult to sort out all the bias or inaccuracy regarding the drug and present an objective statement of facts.

All the facts are not yet in, and research on the drug's effect is continuing. But you may be faced with some personal decision-making regarding the use of marijuana before final answers are known.

You are encouraged, then, to draw some tentative conclusions to guide your actions. The following material should be helpful.

Description and Identification

Marijuana is the name given to the Indian hemp plant *Cannabis sativa*. This plant grows easily in mild climates all over the world, especially in Mexico, Africa, India, and the Middle East. It also grows in the United States. As a drug plant, cannabis is ancient. A Chinese emperor who wrote a book on drugs and their medicinal values in 2737 B.C. described the hemp plant and prescribed the substance *hashish* for a variety of complaints, including malaria and absentmindedness.

As the flowers and seed heads of the hemp plant ripen, a liquid oozes out that is collected and, in this pure state, is known as *hashish*. The dried flowers and leaves are crushed or chopped into small pieces, which are rolled and smoked as cigarettes commonly known as "reefers," "sticks," or "joints." The odor of the smoke is like that of burnt weeds or rope, with a distinct sweetish smell. The strength of a sample of marijuana depends on the part of the plant from which it is made, the soil where it is grown, and the method used in its cultivation and storage. The potency, therefore, varies considerably. A batch of high-potency marijuana is known as "Acapulco Gold." Even this variety, however, is only about one-tenth as strong as hashish, which only rarely is brought into the United States.

Marijuana is dealt with by Federal law as if it were a narcotic. Its effect, however, is that of a mild hallucinogen. It is much less powerful than LSD, DMT, peyote, and mescaline. The plant itself may grow five or more feet tall and each leaf has an odd number of leaflets (3, 5, 7, or 9) with notched edges. Marijuana (the Mexican word meaning Mary Jane) is known as "grass," "pot," "weed," or "tea."

Most of the vast amount of marijuana that reaches the illegal market in the United States is smuggled in from Mexico in "bricks" or "kilos" (weighing 2.2 pounds). The packages are wrapped in several layers of paper or in plastic bags. Marijuana is also carried across the border in small, carefully concealed bags by nonprofessionals, who may bring in enough for their own use and for a pot party or two.

Dependence and Other Effects of Abuse

Marijuana does not result in physical dependence, but many experts report that it can produce serious psychological dependence. This means that the abuser is not driven to repeated use by a physical craving, nor does he suffer withdrawal pains when the drug is withheld; he may, however, develop a compulsive use of marijuana to satisfy a strong psychological need. In addition, the use of marijuana too often leads to experimentation with more dangerous drugs such as barbiturates or opiates and possibly to dependence on them.

A person who begins depending on marijuana as a teen-ager, unfortunately, may never learn how to solve his problems in a realistic way as an adult. A recent study of narcotic addicts in city areas showed that more than 80 per cent of the addicts had previously used marijuana.

The effects of marijuana may vary greatly depending on (1) the strength or potency of the marijuana smoked; (2) the basic personality characteristics of the abuser; (3) the emotions of the abuser at the time of use; and (4) physical conditions at the time of use. When the smoke is inhaled, the active ingredient, THC (tetrahydrocannabinol), passes quickly into the blood stream and begins to affect the brain centers in a matter of minutes. Because of the four variables mentioned above, it is impossible to predict exactly how a person will react to the drug. However, various combinations of the following physical effects are characteristic of a user of marijuana:

reduction of overall body temperature

reduction in ability to coördinate body movements

reduction in glucose

a desire for sweets and a general increase in appetite

nausea

inflammation of mucous membranes

dilated pupils

inaccurate spatial perception. (This false judging of distance is particularly dangerous when the abuser attempts to drive a car.)

Psychological and emotional effects of using marijuana may include various combinations of the following:

giggling and hilarity

laziness, indifference, and carelessness

emotional instability

irritability and a quarrelsome disposition

impaired memory

confusion and making of illogical and faulty decisions

withdrawal from responsibilities and normal social contacts

reduction of inhibitions, and an ignoring of the restraints a normal individual relies upon to check his socially improper, immoral, or illegal impulses

exaggeration of sensory perception

hallucinations (occurring with strong and repeated doses)

anxiety and deep depression (with repeated use).

Those attempting to condone the use of marijuana have developed many arguments to support their cause. Two of the most frequent involve a comparison between marijuana and tobacco and between marijuana and alcohol.

Marijuana or Tobacco

The argument is made that "pot" is not as injurious as tobacco and therefore should be just as available and as exempt from legal restrictions. An opinion on this question depends to a considerable extent on a knowledge of the effects produced by the two substances. Let's look at the similarities and the differences that result from the use of each of these substances.

Neither tobacco nor marijuana produces physical dependence. Both can result in psychological dependence. It is now generally accepted that the continued use of tobacco may result in impaired functioning of heart and lungs and induce cancer or other serious illnesses. Marijuana is not known to do any of these things, although long-term research is not available on marijuana's effects on the human body.

Use of tobacco does not intoxicate the user, make him violent, change his sensory perception, reduce his ability to function normally, cause hallucinations, reduce his inhibitions, or make him a dangerous driver. Marijuana may have any one or a combination of all these effects.

Tobacco may generally be smoked while the user is going about his normal activities and without damaging effect on his mental or emotional responses. This is not true with the use of marijuana.

Finally, the use of tobacco is unlikely to lead to the use of more dangerous substances for "kicks" or consolation.

It is apparent that the user may be "burned" by the smoking of either of these substances but in a very different way. An unbiased reader might decide that it is better to avoid both substances rather than trying to decide which one is better.

Marijuana or Alcohol

There are those who believe that marijuana is safer for the user than alcohol, or certainly no worse. Thus, it has been suggested that if marijuana were legalized, it would be widely accepted as a substitute for alcohol.

This would supposedly reduce consumption of alcohol and the well-known social problems for which it is responsible. The experience in India proved this not to be true. For some time India had strict laws governing the use of alcohol but had no legal restriction on the use of bhang (marijuana). During the "legal period" of marijuana, alcohol control was in no way easier, and there was no indication that those who liked the illegal alcohol switched over to the legal marijuana. If this experience could be applied to our own situation, it would seem fair to say that legalizing the use of marijuana would not substantially improve the alcohol problem.

There are two other points to be noted. The first is that alcohol is a depressant, but marijuana is a mild hallucinogen with both stimulant and depressant properties. A person who has consumed a large quantity of alcohol goes through gradual stages of immobilization to a possible drunken stupor. A person intoxicated with marijuana is likely to become highly active and sometimes to follow a dangerous pattern of behavior. Chronic use of marijuana apparently increases mental instability.

A second point is that many users of alcohol consume it in limited quantities to relax and thus do not even seek or approach a point of intoxication. On the other hand, users of marijuana generally attempt to achieve intoxication.

It is only fair to mention that the use of alcohol does, all too often, lead to problem drinking or alcoholism. It is not now thought that the use of marijuana will result in such a serious form of physical and psychological dependence as does alcohol. It should be kept in mind, however, that the availability of marijuana is not likely to reduce alcohol consumption. Marijuana is of no use in treating alcoholism. The drug has been known for hundreds of years and researchers have found no medical use for it. As with tobacco, the wise young person might reach the conclusion that the choice between alcohol and drugs is a very poor one and it is best to avoid both.

The Question of Legalizing Marijuana

An increasing number of young Americans, estimated well into the thousands, are being arrested each year because of their involvement with marijuana. Even so, there is little apparent curtailment of the problem. Thus, there is considerable pressure from some sources to legalize the use of marijuana.

Is it not reasonable, however, that any action to liberalize the use of this substance should be based on rational considerations and proven facts? Unfortunately, many of the facts about the physical and psychological effects of marijuana are not known at this time. Medical research on the effects of marijuana is relatively new. To be sure of the effects may take many years.

As you know, the very serious consequences of smoking tobacco were not recognized or publicized until hundreds of years after tobacco was first used—and after untold numbers of "uneducated" smokers had died from conditions now known to be directly related to smoking cigarettes.

Some Medical and Legal Views

At the present time, doctors of the American Medical Association's Council on Mental Health feel there is sufficient evidence to state that when used over a period of time marijuana is harmful.

Some recent research at the National Institute of Mental Health tested the effects of a new chemical that copies the active ingredient of marijuana. When the individuals tested were given several doses over a short period of time, immediate reactions were severe in each of the persons tested. Even with lesser amounts of the chemical, several individuals, for unknown reasons, had feelings of depression, fear, and panic.

Objective studies and research of this kind, all scientists agree, will help answer basic questions about the special drug qualities of marijuana, how it works in the body, and how it produces its effects.

In the matter of legal opinion today, anyone who uses marijuana is engaging in an activity punishable by law as a crime. Such an activity must be regarded as something more serious than innocent experimentation.

Narcotics

he term *narcotics* refers to the so-called hard drugs that characteristically produce a state of euphoria, tranquillity, drowsiness, unconsciousness, or sleep. The use of narcotics goes back to ancient times when it was somehow discovered that the hardened milky juice or gum from the seed-pod of a certain kind of poppy would produce the above effects when it was eaten or smoked in a pipe.

This brown poppy-gum contained *opium*, which is still the source of most present-day narcotics, including morphine, heroin, and codeine.

Opium

pium, a product of the opium poppy, was used by the Egyptians as far back as 1500 B.C.; from that time on, its abuse has appeared in various parts of the world as a challenging and serious social problem.

The first anti-opium law in America was passed in 1875 in the form of a city ordinance in San Francisco. Today, opium itself is not a significant problem in this country, but morphine, heroin, and the other narcotics obtained from opium offer serious difficulties in their control.

The effects of all the substances that are derived from opium are quite similar; these effects are discussed in detail in the section on heroin.

Morphine

orphine was first extracted from opium in 1805. Because it makes the user sleepy, it was appropriately named after Morpheus, the Greek god of dreams.

Morphine is an odorless white substance made up of fine crystals. Abusers call it "M," "Miss Emma," "white stuff," or by some local slang term. Although morphine is widely used, it has taken second place to heroin among drug abusers. The most common methods of using morphine are swallowing it and injecting it.

Morphine has a very valuable use in medicine in relieving severe pain. It also has at least two very dangerous properties. One is that, even with medical supervision, its use can cause physical and psychological dependence. The second is the hazard of a deadly overdose from this very powerful drug.

Heroin

eroin is by far the greatest problem-substance in narcotic abuse. Of those dependent on hard drugs, about 92 per cent are heroin users. The drug is produced by the introduction of an inexpensive chemical into morphine. This results in heroin, which is actually several times more powerful than morphine.

A kilo (2.2 pounds) of pure heroin has a value of between ten and fifteen thousand dollars. When this kilo is "cut," or diluted, with substances like powdered milk or powdered sugar, the mixture ends up containing 3 or 4 per cent heroin. A little arithmetic shows that, with such "cutting," the original kilo will grow into a product worth a million dollars on the illicit market.

DEPENDENCE AND OTHER EFFECTS OF ABUSE

Heroin is known to abusers by such names as "H," "horse," and "junk." It is usually injected or sniffed. Heroin, which is illegal in the United States, produces the same general effects as all the other narcotics. Its immediate effects include

a dulling of the senses, including pain
a depressing of the central nervous system
grogginess
sense of well-being
lack of coördination
impaired thinking
drop in blood pressure
slowing of respiration and circulation
stupor or coma.

Less immediate effects of the continuing use of heroin include these physical reactions:

loss of appetite
malnutrition and serious loss of weight
constipation.

Heroin produces both physical and psychological dependence with unusual speed, and tolerance to the drug is built up rapidly so that the dosage must be constantly increased.

The abuser is never sure how strong a dose he is taking, and this always carries the risk of death. In addition, there are secondary dangers that may be as serious as the reactions to heroin itself. A majority of users, when getting a "fix," or dosage, do so by "shooting" the drug directly into a vein with a hypodermic syringe. Unsterilized needles can spread hepatitis, tetanus, and other infections; and blood poisoning is not uncommon. The walls of the veins break down from repeated puncturing; abscesses form, forcing the abuser to inject the heroin into alternate veins of his body. Permanent scar tissue from repeated injections is a telltale sign which the user must keep covered in order to avoid detection.

In reviewing the damage that use of a hypodermic needle causes, it is interesting to note that when this method was first developed, it was thought the needle would eliminate what was then known as "addiction." This reasoning was based on the theory that the human system could develop a taste and a craving for the narcotic only if the narcotic were introduced through the stomach; but if the heroin were injected directly into the blood stream, this "addiction" would not occur. We now know this theory was completely false.

Those who try to "kick the habit" and escape from its control are in for some torturous reactions when the drug is withdrawn. This material from *Drug Abuse* (California State Department of Education) describes the symptoms of withdrawal.

"Several hours after the last dose, the addict feels his habit coming on and begins to yawn, to sweat, and to suffer running of the eyes and nose as though he had an acute head cold. These symptoms increase in severity and are followed, after about 24 hours, by violent muscle spasms and waves of gooseflesh; dilation of the pupils, vomiting, and diarrhea; functions which have been depressed are now hyperactive. The respiration rate is elevated, blood pressure and temperature are heightened, and basal metabolism is accelerated. The flow of body fluids is overabundant. These symptoms may last for two or three days and then diminish gradually over a period of a week or more. The addict may suffer a general feeling of discomfort for several months."

Abrupt and complete withdrawal of the drug from a person with a strong physical dependence on it results in great physical torment and may be fatal. Even if the very painful physical experience of withdrawal is endured, the abuser, because of his psychological dependence, may, in a weak moment, start the habit again and yet again. Unfortunately, few permanent cures are accomplished.

A final problem faces the person who is dependent upon heroin and other narcotics. He must pay in cash for his expensive habit—each day. Since the body develops a tolerance to the substance, the quantity needed increases and so does the cost of his drug supply. The abuser needs more money yet is less able to hold a steady job. He is likely to do almost anything to maintain his drug supply. This may result in the abuser's turning to various criminal activities to support the habit that he has no real hope of permanently breaking.

Codeine

Codeine can be derived directly from opium or prepared from morphine. It is an effective pain reliever, and it is also used extensively as an ingredient of cough medicine. Because codeine does not produce euphoria as effectively as heroin or morphine, it is not in as great demand by abusers. Codeine does produce both physical and psychological dependence. Many states are passing laws restricting its use, because some abusers, finding it available at reasonable cost in cough syrups and without legal complication, were discovered to be drinking the cough medicine by the bottle.

Methadone and Meperidine

An unfortunate peculiarity of drugs with powerful pain-killing qualities is that they can also produce a dangerous dependence in those who use them. Chemists are constantly looking for and trying to develop a pain killer which is also harmless. Methadone and meperidine are but two of the hundreds of drugs that have been developed in this search. Both are sold under legal restrictions, however, because like all the other true *opiates*, or products of opium, they can produce dependence.

Methadone may offer some hope in treatment of heroin and morphine dependence; it has been found that during treatment for drug dependence when methadone is substituted for heroin or morphine it produces less-painful withdrawal illness than these two more-powerful drugs. It is being used only experimentally, however, for this purpose.

Cocaine

A description of cocaine might have been included in the chapter on stimulants, because, unlike all the other narcotics, it stimulates rather than depresses the central nervous system. Cocaine is discussed in this chapter, however, because it is legally classified as a narcotic, and it is not uncommon for an abuser to mix it with either heroin or morphine for an injection known as a "speedball." Strong psychological dependence develops with its use.

Cocaine is usually found as a white, odorless, fluffy powder. Its appearance results in the slang name of "snow." A user of cocaine may be called a "snowbird," and the act of inhaling is described as "snuffing the snow." Cocaine also has many other slang names such as "C," "coke," and "dust."

The crystals are obtained from the leaves of coca, a South American plant, and are either sniffed or injected directly into the blood stream. The immediate effects are

intense excitement
euphoria
sense of great physical strength and mental
    power
tremors.

These first reactions are later replaced by symptoms such as these:

anxiety and possible feelings of persecution
depression
hallucinations
convulsions.

Repeated use of cocaine may result in aggressive and criminal behavior.

The chronic abuser may also suffer some unusual physical symptoms. He may have the awful feeling that insects are crawling under his skin which causes him to tear at himself in an effort to get rid of them.

Who Takes Narcotics?

Unlike the use of other substances that can cause dependence, narcotics abuse is largely localized in areas where certain social situations exist. Figures from the Bureau of Narcotics and Dangerous Drugs show that:

New York City has nearly 50 per cent of all individuals who are dependent on narcotics in this country.

If New York City and Chicago were combined, they would account for over 61 per cent of the cases of dependence.

If Los Angeles and Detroit were added to the first two cities, 66⅔ per cent of known cases would be included.

If the number of known abusers in the top ten cities of the United States were totaled, the figure would account for 75 per cent of all those dependent on narcotics.

In general, narcotics abuse is, as you can see, a problem of the big urban areas. In New York City, it seems to occur most frequently in the poverty areas of the city. Is it not reasonable that people in highly depressed areas feel more deeply a need to escape, even temporarily and artificially, from the misery of their surroundings? And is it not possible that, in the hopelessness of their situation, drug-induced dreams and fantasies are about as close as many may ever come to the good things of life for which they yearn? These questions are not in support of narcotics abuse but they may provide a clue to corrective measures.

It is important to note, however, that use of narcotics, though most common in depressed urban areas, is being found with increasing frequency in middle- and upper-class neighborhoods. It thus seems obvious that the causes of drug dependence lie not only in an economically deprived environment; they may lie in any unfavorable environment, as well as in the personality of the abuser himself.

In any case, whenever or wherever narcotics are misused, the result is a wretched and unhealthy existence for the abuser and one from which he may never be able to free himself.

Volatile Chemicals

A volatile chemical is a substance that changes easily into a vapor gas. Among the volatile substances being misused are glue, paint thinner, gasoline, and lighter fluid. Deliberately inhaling or sniffing the fumes of the solvents present can produce effects that are as wild and dangerous as those resulting from swallowing or injecting drugs and narcotics. However, the volatile substances are not classified as either drugs or narcotics. A further difference is that they are generally easy to obtain legally and at prices that are not inflated by the illegal market.

Glue

The glue used by glue-sniffers is the plastic cement that comes in a tube and is often called "airplane glue" by model makers. Toluene is the solvent in glue that produces the effects upon the abuser and that is so very dangerous. The fumes are generally inhaled from a rag which is kept soaked with the glue or from a plastic or paper bag into which the glue has been squeezed.

DEPENDENCE AND OTHER
EFFECTS OF ABUSE

Glue-sniffers are in definite danger of psychological dependence, and some of the more severe cases report physical problems upon withdrawal. In addition, the body builds up a tolerance to the fumes and the abuser must inhale increasing amounts.

Glue-sniffing produces the following physical and mental effects:

a tingling sensation
intoxication, with slurred speech, dizziness, and unsteady gait
irritability
irresponsible, foolish, and sometimes homicidal actions
possible loss of consciousness and coma
inflamed eyes and swollen nose, throat, and lung tissue
nausea, vomiting, appetite and weight loss.

Continued sniffing of glue is extremely dangerous and results in the following:

blood abnormalities and destruction of bone marrow
damage to brain, nervous system, kidneys, liver, and heart.

Any of the above may result in death.

Fatalities have also occurred from suffocation resulting from plastic bags being held by the intoxicated glue-sniffer against his face until he is unconscious—and dies.

WHO ARE THE GLUE-SNIFFERS?

Records show that the glue-sniffer is often younger than abusers of narcotics and other drugs. As you will see from the chart that appears on page 34, it is more likely to be the younger brother or sister than the teenager in the family who "gets stuck on glue." Glue-sniffing seems to be more common among members of low-economic groups, although older youngsters and those from middle-class to wealthy families may also become involved.

Some
common
characteristics
of
glue-sniffers

•

High proportion of boys

•

Some users as young as 8, with an average age of about 14

•

Found in certain school areas and among some low-economic groups

•

Lack of parental supervision and control

•

Abusers usually introduced to habit by schoolmates or friends

•

Abuse usually accompanied by irregular school attendance, running away from home, or other antisocial behavior

•

Often followed by violent or erratic activities (including serious falls, car accidents, aggressive behavior)

Other Volatile Liquids

There are scores of liquids that give off fumes, and abusers have found that most of them can produce effects similar to those mentioned for glue. Some volatile liquids used for these effects are lacquer and lacquer thinner, shellac, carbon tetrachloride, kerosene, benzene, ether, and marking-pencil fluid.

When these fluids are properly used for intended purposes, in an open area with good ventilation, the fumes may be noticeable or even objectionable to the user, but they are not generally dangerous under these conditions. The deliberate inhaling of these concentrated fumes for a period of time is entirely different and is extremely dangerous.

Still other substances that abusers have employed are the aerosol sprays. To make the aerosol can or bomb, a liquid substance is placed in a sealed container under gas pressure which, when activated by the pushing of a button valve, sends forth a fine mist or spray. Manufacturers have shown great imagination in packaging into aerosol containers most of the volatile liquids already mentioned—and a great number of other liquids as well. While reports do not indicate that thrill-seekers are inhaling the aerosol mist of such known poisons as disinfectants, insect sprays, and weed killers, there have been instances of persons inhaling other types of aerosol fog to the point of unconsciousness. A coolant which has as its purpose the instant chilling of drinks seems particularly hazardous.

Most of the substances used by drug abusers such as marijuana, LSD, stimulants, depressants, and narcotics are strictly controlled by law. This, of course, is not generally the case with glue and other volatile chemicals, although some states are enacting legislation that places restrictions on the sale of dangerous types of glue.

Because of the great number of common and highly useful chemical products that are volatile, it is impossible to prevent the inhaling of toxic fumes by restricting the sale of the products. Any real progress in preventing the "sniffing practice" must be achieved by educating the potential abuser about the severe hazards involved.

The Law and Drug Control

If laws alone could control the use—and abuse—of drugs and other dangerous substances, we would have no problem. There are international treaties, Federal statutes, state laws, and local ordinances to cover all aspects of the drug problem. By and large, the Federal regulations deal with the importation, production, and sale of these substances. State and local laws may also cover these, but their emphasis is on the *possession*, *sale*, and *use* of drugs and on *penalties* for violations.

Specific Laws on Drug Abuse

Each young person is encouraged to check into his local and state laws. But no matter in which of the 50 states you live, you are subject to specific laws that deal with the drug problem. (For some information on major drug-abuse laws enacted by the Federal government, see the chart on page 38.) These laws govern the following aspects:

legal and illegal importation
preparation, production, and manufacture
    (including the growing of plants that
    supply necessary ingredients)
transportation and distribution
purchase, sale, and possession
legal and illegal use (including the issuing
    and recording of prescriptions).

Specific laws also cover the procedures of search and seizure, arrest, trial, and the penalties for conviction. In addition to bail, legal fees, fines, and prison terms to which a drug abuser is subject, he must also face other consequences of breaking the law. For example, because strong enforcement of drug laws forces him to "go underground," the abuser must be in direct or indirect contact with professional drug "pushers," who care only for their own safety and high profits.

The Drug "Pusher"

Invariably, the legal penalties for "pushing" are the most severe of all. "Pushers" know this and are ruthless in their relations with others in order to protect themselves.

Every person who knows of the experimenter's illegal actions is a potential informer. Because preferential treatment may be given to the one who supplies information about misuse of drugs, it is the rare abuser who will not try to save himself by informing on his "friends." The most productive source of information available to the police on drug sources and drug users is an arrested abuser.

The Drug Abuser

A record of an arrest involving drugs or narcotics can follow an individual and handicap him in many ways for the rest of his life.

A common question that appears on almost all employment application blanks is: "Have you ever been convicted of any crime

Federal laws for the control of drugs

Name of Legislation	Date	Summary of Coverage and Intent of Legislation
Harrison Act	1914	First Federal legislation to regulate and control the production, importation, sale, purchase, or free distribution of opium or drugs that are derived from opium
Narcotic Drugs Import and Export Act	1922	Legislation intended to eliminate the use of narcotics in this country except for legitimate purposes
Marijuana Tax Act	1937	Provides controls over marijuana similar to the controls the Harrison Act has over narcotics
Opium Poppy Control Act	1942	Prohibits the growing of opium poppies in the United States except under license
Boggs Act	1951	Establishes mandatory, severe penalties for conviction on narcotics charges
Narcotics Control Act	1956	Legislation intended to impose very severe penalties for those convicted on narcotics or marijuana charges
Drug Abuse Control Amendments	1965	Adopts strict controls over stimulants, depressants, LSD, and similar substances with provisions to add new substances as the need arises

Enforcement of Federal drug-control laws

In April of 1968, the Bureau of Narcotics and the Bureau of Drug Abuse Control were consolidated into the Bureau of Narcotics and Dangerous Drugs. This new bureau, together with the Bureau of Customs, has major responsibility for the enforcement of Federal drug-control laws.

other than a minor traffic violation?" Once the answer to this question is "Yes," it must always be "Yes."

A record of trustworthiness is a requirement for employment in government jobs and with firms having government contracts. Such a record is difficult to establish for an individual who has been involved with drugs.

Private business is also understandably reluctant to hire anyone who has been convicted for the use of dangerous drugs. Qualities in demand by employers, such as loyalty, perseverance, promptness, and hard work, are not normally associated with a person who has demonstrated a weakness for drugs. So once again the drug abuser is at a severe disadvantage.

Many private and public high schools, colleges, and universities will not accept for admission, or will expel, any student convicted for the use of narcotics or other dangerous drugs. With education an essential in this modern world, a few unwise moments can result in lifelong regrets.

A convicted narcotics offender is often placed on probation. He is strictly supervised and required to register as an addict wherever he goes. Other rights, freedoms, and privileges may also be denied to the convicted drug abuser. He may be rejected in certain fraternal groups and other organizations. He may be unable to seek public office. He may be refused a passport and he may even have his right to vote restricted.

Although some of the treatment that the abuser receives may seem cruel and unjust, it is a harsh reality that many people do not trust him or want to be associated with him.

THE LAW IS CLEAR,
THE PENALTIES ARE SEVERE,
THE ODDS ARE POOR,
      BUT
THE CHOICE IS YOURS!

All too often, one's important decisions are made on the spur of the moment. When you are under no stress of immediate temptation or any pressure to conform to the crowd, however, you can thoughtfully determine the stand you will take if you are ever confronted with a problem associated with drug abuse.

When an important decision is to be made, the following steps are suggested:

1. Assemble facts and seek expert opinion.
2. Face the issues and risks with honesty.
3. Examine and weigh the personal and social implications.
4. Analyze the above in a deliberate and open-minded way.
5. Arrive at a firm decision through this thoughtful process.

Drug Abuse—a Problem Of the Individual

Whether to experiment with dangerous drugs or to avoid their use is a personal decision. Remember that the penalties for experimentation are also very personal. Despite attempts at law enforcement, opportunities to use such substances may be frequent and even unavoidable. The time to make a decision is before immediate and pressing temptation occurs. Facts, reason, logic, and good judgment should determine your decision.

Drug Abuse—a Problem Of Society

A society which has a major problem of drug abuse—and ours does—must consider the consequences and seek corrective measures. The loss of physical, mental, and occupational competence that results from drug abuse is a heavy drain on human resources. The criminal activities associated with drug abuse are also a menace. Abusers are not in a position to solve the problems they create; society as a whole must assume this difficult task.

Drug Abuse—a Legal Problem

Because almost all substances used by drug abusers are either completely outlawed or clearly restricted by law, the moment a person becomes involved in their sale, purchase, possession, or use he is breaking a Federal, state, or local law. The abuser is under the constant pressure of discovery by law-enforcement officials, and the possibility is great that he will eventually be apprehended and will have to suffer the consequences of his actions.

If our present controls are failing, what laws should we have? How can these laws be enforced? How severe should the penalties for drug abuse be? These are all questions that must be faced if drug abuse is to be successfully controlled.

Drug Abuse—a Medical And Psychological Problem

*B*ecause drug dependence results from practices that disregard or defy the law, it may be thought of by some as only a law-enforcement problem. But it is a public health problem as well.

Drug dependence is a chronic disease which the abuser has "caught" from other abusers and which he is likely to spread through his personal contacts with still others. In a real sense, drug dependence is communicable and contagious.

What are the personality weaknesses that make an individual particularly susceptible? How can we develop the attitudes and the strengths necessary for immunity? How can the abuser be restored to health? These are medical and psychological problems that still require a great deal of research.

Physical and/or Psychological Dependence

*M*uch is sometimes made of the point that there is no real need for concern about the use of some substances such as marijuana and LSD because they apparently do not result in physical dependence. If, however, a person has a compulsive habit which is destructive to him and others but which he has not the power to break, is there any real importance in how the dependence is classified?

The Danger of Ignorance

*W*hen drugs that can be misused are obtained in ways other than through a medical prescription, they must be secured illegally. Strength and purity are therefore unknown. The abuser has no way of knowing exactly what he is taking or the strength of it, and death may result from this ignorance. In the illegal drug market, normal practices of cleanliness in producing, handling, and packaging are largely ignored. It is unlikely that a producer or supplier who is already breaking the law would be concerned about the rigorous sanitary standards required of legal manufacturers. An abuser must put his trust and even his life into the hands of a "pusher," a person who himself has purchased his product from an illegal source. There is no such thing as a "reputable" dealer with whom to do business.

Unpredictable And Uncontrollable Reactions

*S*ome people tan; others sunburn. Some can eat strawberries; others get hives. Some individuals get poison ivy by brushing against the plant; others can touch it without being affected. This is to say that each person is unique and may have different physical and/or emotional reactions to the same thing. Individuals have different phobias, allergies, tolerances, and susceptibilities. These are unpredictable and largely uncontrollable. In the case of drugs, of course, *all* users are affected —even if temporarily. What is more, drug experimentation with powerful substances tests individual reactions in a completely unnecessary and highly dangerous way.

Extended or Recurring Reactions

The immediate effects of most substances that cause dependence last from four to twelve hours. This may not be the limit of the time involved, however. Mental, emotional, or physical damage may require extended periods of treatment. Dependence may never be completely eliminated. And, of course, death from an overdose is a constant hazard.

LSD has an additional reaction that is not understood by medical authorities. It is the recurrence of all the original sensory hallucinations of sound, color, and shapes long after the first effects of the dosage have worn off. This "flashback," which may come months later, is unpredictable, unpreventable, and highly disturbing to the one experiencing it. The abuser may wonder if he is losing his mind, and there is some reason to believe that in fact he is.

Loss of Purpose and Energy

Use of the substances that can cause dependence can weaken or destroy the abuser's physical and emotional energy. Obtaining and using drugs becomes his main concern. Those standards and values that once seemed important lose significance, and he joins a subculture of abusers. To say that an abuser becomes more creative or productive is inaccurate when tested by objective measures. The person's life takes on new direction— often down a dead-end street. His carefully laid plans are disrupted, his original goals are unimportant, and his future is in jeopardy.

Impaired Judgment

Narcotics and other dangerous drugs are usually taken by an abuser so that he will feel different. These substances change the way his senses report messages and the way the brain interprets the messages. Information concerning distance, rate of movement, size, odor, color, sound, and pain is likely to be received and interpreted by the brain in inaccurate fashion. Not only are these physical judgments distorted but moral judgments of right or wrong are badly impaired, as are judgments involving caution versus foolhardiness. It is easy to see why behavior may become bizarre or dangerous.

A Traffic Hazard

The user of drugs and other dangerous substances is a serious traffic hazard, both as a pedestrian and as a driver. Slow reaction time, acute irritability, impaired depth perception, faulty judgment, drowsiness, illusions, intoxication, and poor coördination greatly reduce the abuser's ability to survive even in normal traffic conditions. And the survival chances of those whom he meets on the highway diminish as well.

A Criminal Record

When a person becomes involved with the abuse of drugs he is usually breaking a law. Names of those arrested appear almost daily in the newspapers. A police record for a violation involving these illegal substances can permanently damage an abuser's future in the areas of employment, education, membership in various organizations, and social acceptance.

The Extravagant Cost

Experimentation with some "forbidden substance" has led many into an uncontrollable habit that ultimately requires every cent the abuser can lay his hands on. The effects of many of these substances do not in themselves cause criminal acts, but the need for money to support the habit often forces the abuser into some form of criminal activity. The abuser may suddenly find himself in danger of being arrested twice—first, for theft, burglary, assault, and/or other illegal acts to obtain money to pay for the drugs; and secondly, for possession or use of the drugs themselves.

Cost is not restricted to paying for the day-to-day needs of the abuser. Consideration must also be given to community welfare and medical costs of those who are unemployable because of their complete engrossment with the subculture of drugs.

Another item of cost cannot be ignored. This applies to those who seek to break their dependence on dangerous substances and "rejoin the world." Rehabilitation is not easily achieved. Treatment is usually extensive and expensive. And this highly specialized professional attention is very costly, whether a cure results or not.

The Ultimate Question

All of us have problems. Sometimes the burden is very heavy. Substances that offer us escape from unpleasant realities have their appeal. However, there is one big catch. The relief provided by drugs lasts only a brief time. Drug abuse in no way solves or reduces the original problem but adds a new and bigger problem to the user's list of troubles. Ask yourself:

Will the real
Or imagined benefits
That a potential drug abuser hopes for
Ever outweigh the problems
That a drug abuser faces
For the rest of his life?

Glossary

Many of the words included in this glossary have more than one meaning. The definition given here helps clarify the meaning of each word as used in the context of *DRUGS: Facts on Their Use and Abuse*.

abuse (ə būs′). This term refers to the misuse of drugs or other substances by a person who has usually obtained them illegally and administers them himself without medical advice or supervision.

addiction (ə dik′shən). *See* physical dependence.

amphetamines (am fet′ə mēnz), drugs which stimulate the central nervous system. They are often called "pep pills" and include drugs with such trade names as Benzedrine, Dexedrine, and Methedrine.

barbiturates (bär bich′ə rāts), drugs which depress the action of the central nervous system and act as sedatives. The names of most such drugs end in "al" as in the case of secobarbital, amobarbital, and phenobarbital. These drugs are sold under many trade names such as Seconal, Amytal, and Nembutal.

Cannabis sativa (kan′ə bis sə tē′və), the Indian hemp plant whose resin and parts are used throughout the world and known by such names as marijuana, hashish, bhang, and kif.

chromosomes (krō′mə sōms), the threadlike bodies in a cell which carry the genes that control hereditary characteristics.

cocaine (kō kān′), a white, odorless powder obtained from the leaves of the South American coca shrub; acts locally as an anesthetic and on the central nervous system as a stimulant.

compulsion (kəm pul′shən), a compelling, irresistible impulse which causes a person to act in a way that may be contrary to his good judgment, training, or normal desire.

congenital (kən jen′ə tl), existing from birth.

contraindication (kon′trə in′də kā′shən), an indication that a particular treatment or procedure is medically inadvisable.

convulsion (kən vul′shən), an involuntary, uncontrollable muscular contortion.

dependence (di pen′dəns), the need for and reliance upon a substance. *See* psychological dependence *and* physical dependence.

depressant (di pres′nt), a substance having the quality of reducing or lowering the mental and/or physical vitality or functioning of an individual.

drug abuse. *See* abuse.

glucose (glü′kōs), the end product of the digestion of starches and sugars, which forms the body's chief source of energy.

habituation (hə bich′ü ā′shən). *See* psychological dependence.

hallucination (hə lü′sn ā′shən), a sensory experience which does not exist outside the mind of an individual and is a false perception of the real conditions.

hallucinogen (hə lü′sn ə jen′), refers to any substance that produces hallucinations.

hallucinogenic (hə lü′sn ə jen′ik), causing or producing hallucinations.

heroin (her′ō in), a narcotic in the form of a white, crystalline powder, the manufacture and importation of which are prohibited in this country by Federal law.

45

intoxication (in tok′sə kā′shən), the temporary reduction of mental and physical control or the stupefaction of normal functions because of the effects of drugs, alcohol, or other substances.

kilo (kē′lō), an abbreviation for kilogram, which is a measure of weight equal to 1000 grams or 2.2 pounds.

LSD (lysergic acid diethylamide) (lī sėr′jik as′id dī eth ə lam′īd), a hallucinogenic drug which has highly dangerous properties. LSD is not legally produced in the United States.

marijuana or **marihuana** (mar′ə wä′na), the dried flowering tops and leaves of the female Indian hemp plant, *Cannabis sativa*, commonly called pot, grass, weed, tea.

mescaline (mes′kə lēn), the active ingredient in the peyote cactus; hallucinogenic drug.

methamphetamine (meth′am fet′ə mēn), one of the amphetamine drugs. The most common methamphetamine in drug abuse in the United States is Methedrine, nicknamed Speed by drug abusers.

morphine (môr′fēn), a white, bitter powder derived from the narcotic opium. It is widely used in medicine to relieve pain and induce sleep, but it is also used by drug abusers and is highly addictive.

narcotic (när kot′ik), a drug that is capable of producing drowsiness, sleep, unconsciousness, or stupor. Such drugs blunt the senses and can cause physical and psychological dependence.

opium (ō′pē əm), the milky juice of the seedpod of the opium poppy that has narcotic and analgesic properties and from which morphine, codeine, and heroin are derived. These substances are known as opiates.

paranoid (par′ə noid), a person suffering from mental disorder in which he has unsubstantiated fears that others are threatening him or are hostile to him.

peyote (pā ō′tē), a variety of cactus containing the hallucinogenic ingredient mescaline.

pharmacology (fär′mə kol′ə jē), the science dealing with the production, use, and effects of drugs.

physical dependence (fiz′ə kl di pen′dəns). This was formerly known as addiction and has the following two characteristics: (1) the development of a body tolerance which requires progressively larger doses to produce the desired effect, and (2) extremely painful withdrawal illness when the drug is withheld.

psilocybin (sil ə si′bin), the psychedelic chemical in the psilocybe mushroom which acts as a hallucinogen.

psychedelic (adj. and n.) (sī′kə del′ik), a drug such as LSD, psilocybin, or mescaline; or to the intensified perception of the senses which these drugs produce.

psychiatrist (sī kī′ə trist), a physician who specializes in the treatment of mental disorders.

psychological dependence (sī′kə loj′ə kl di pen′dəns). This is sometimes known as habituation or psychic dependence. It refers to the persistent desire for a substance which may border on compulsion. It often occurs simultaneously with physical dependence and of the two is frequently more complex and difficult to cure.

psychosis (sī kō′sis) (n.), psychotic (sī kot′ik) (adj.), any severe mental disorder or disease.

psychotic (sī kot′ik), relating to or caused by severe mental disorder or disease.

schizophrenia (skiz′ə frē′nē ə), a mental disease marked by loss of contact with reality and disintegration of personality.

stimulant (stim′yə lənt), a substance which temporarily speeds up the action of the central nervous system.

tolerance (tol′ər əns), the ability of the body to adapt itself to a poison so that it can endure or tolerate it. The building up of tolerance to a substance requires increasingly larger doses in order to obtain the effects originally produced by its use.

toluene (tol′ yú ēn), a highly volatile solvent, a main ingredient of most glues and plastic cement.

volatile liquid (vol′ə tl lik′wid), a liquid that changes rapidly and easily into a vapor as in the case of the evaporation of gasoline.

withdrawal illness (wiŦH drô′əl il′nis), the extremely painful symptoms that an abuser suffers when a substance upon which his system has become physically dependent is withheld.

Reading List

Bloomquist, E. R., M.D. *Marijuana*. Glencoe Press, 1968.

The Crutch That Cripples—Drug Dependence. Committee on Alcoholism and Drug Dependence and Council on Mental Health, American Medical Association, Chicago, Illinois 60610, 1967.

Hyde, Margaret O., Editor. *Mind Drugs*. McGraw-Hill Book Company, New York, N.Y. 10036, 1968.

National Institute of Mental Health. "*Hooked!*" PHS #1610, U.S. Department of HEW, Supt. of Documents, U.S. Government Printing Office, Washington, D.C. 20402, 1967.

_____. *LSD: Some Questions and Answers*. PHS #1828, U.S. Department of HEW, Supt. of Documents, U.S. Government Printing Office, Washington, D.C. 20402, 1968.

_____. *Marihuana: Some Questions and Answers*. PHS #1829, U.S. Department of HEW, Supt. of Documents, U.S. Government Printing Office, Washington, D.C. 20402, 1968.

_____. *The Up and Down Drugs: Amphetamines and Barbiturates*. PHS #1830, U.S. Department of HEW, Supt. of Documents, U.S. Government Printing Office, Washington, D.C. 20402, 1968.

Vogel, Victor H., and Vogel, Virginia E. *Facts About Narcotics and Other Dangerous Drugs*. Science Research Associates, Chicago, Illinois 60611, 1967.

Blairsville Junior High School
Blairsville, Pennsylvania